Stories fɪ

OLD TESTAMENI

Sally Ann Wright and Honor Ayres

When the world began

Before anything else was made, God was there in the darkness.

God made light to shine in the darkness and saw that it was good.

God shaped the land so there were snow-topped mountains, and deep blue seas.

God filled the land with flowering plants and fruit-bearing trees.

God made the hot sun to give light by day and the silvery moon and stars to light up the night sky.

God filled the sea with colourful creatures large and small and the air with buzzing bees and bright birds that sang.

God filled the earth with lumbering elephants and long-necked giraffes, with big cats covered in patterns and stripes, and rhinos, antelope, deer, rabbits and tiny mice. God made the first man and woman. They were called Adam and Eve.

God talked to Adam and Eve and they talked to him. God wanted them to enjoy his world and be his friends.

God looked at the world he had made and it was beautiful. Then God rested.

The whispering snake

God made a garden for Adam and Eve to
live in and asked them to take care of all the
animals. He told them they could
eat anything they wanted, except
the fruit from one tree.

But the snake came
and whispered to Eve.
He showed her how good
the fruit on that one tree looked. Suddenly it
seemed better than all the other fruit God had
given them.

Eve took a big, deep bite. Then she shared
it with Adam.

Adam and Eve looked at each other. They felt
guilty. They realised they had done the one thing
God had told them not to do. They had
spoilt everything.

Now they were unhappy. And God was unhappy.
They couldn't stay any longer in the garden God had
made for them. They couldn't be his special friends
any more.

Noah's floating zoo

God's beautiful world was spoiled. The people God had made could not live together happily. They did not share. They were not kind to each other. They were selfish and they were greedy. They cared only about themselves.

They started to fight and hurt each other. They took things that belonged to someone else. They forgot about God and about how to love and care for other people.

God was sad. But there was one man who was good. Noah still loved God. He tried to love other people and care for his family and the world God had made.

God told Noah to build an ark, a big boat that would float on the waters.

Noah filled the ark with birds and animals of every kind. Soon there would be rain, and the rain would become a flood that would wash the whole earth clean again.

When Noah, his family and all the animals were safe inside the ark, the rain began to fall. It rained and it rained and it rained.

The rivers burst their banks and the seas flooded the land. But Noah's ark floated on the water.

When the rain stopped and dry land at last appeared again, God told Noah and the animals they could leave the ark. A bright rainbow filled the sky.

Noah thanked God for keeping them safe. And God promised there would never be another flood like it.

A baby called 'laughter'

Abraham and Sarah were happy in Canaan. But there was one thing missing. God had promised them a big family. Their goats had kids. Their sheep had lambs. Their camels had baby camels. But they still didn't have any children.

Abraham looked up at the stars in the night sky.

'Don't worry,' he heard God say. 'You will have children. One day your family will be as many as the stars you can see above you!'

Weeks passed. Months passed. Years passed. Abraham and Sarah thought they were too old now to have children.

But still Abraham trusted God. And then Sarah had a lovely baby boy. They were so happy, they called him Isaac, which means 'laughter'.

Abraham looked again at the stars and smiled. God had kept his promise.

Joseph the favourite son

Jacob loved his wife Rachel very much. But he had three other wives too, and a big family of twelve sons and a daughter. His favourite child was Joseph.

When Joseph was seventeen, Jacob gave him a beautiful, brightly coloured coat. This made Joseph's brothers jealous. They wished Jacob loved them half as much.

Then, one day, they found a way to get rid of Joseph. While out taking care of their father's sheep, they sold him to some traders who were on their way to Egypt!

If that was not enough, they took his beautiful coat and dipped it in goat's blood. Then they returned

to their father, pretending to be sad. They showed
him the coat and the blood – and poor Jacob thought
his favourite son had been killed by a wild animal!

But God had plans for Joseph.

A very happy family

God looked after Joseph while he was in Egypt.

When the king had strange dreams that kept him awake at night, Joseph was brought to help him understand what they meant. Through those dreams,

God showed Joseph how he could help himself, and all the people of Egypt.

For seven years there would be good harvests and plenty of food for everyone. But then there would be seven years when no one would have enough to eat. The king made sure Joseph was in charge so that food could be saved and shared so that no one would go hungry.

It worked so well that Joseph's brothers in Canaan came to Egypt for food. What a surprise they had when they found that their little brother was there to help them! Jacob was overjoyed to find his son was still alive, and the whole family came to live in the land of Egypt.

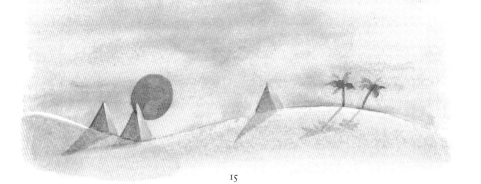

Miriam and the princess

Kings came and went, and soon the Egyptians forgot how Joseph had helped them.

God's people were made to be slaves. They had to work hard for the king. And when baby boys were born, soldiers came to take them away from their mothers.

When Jochebed's baby son was born, she decided to hide him. At first it was easy, but soon he made too much noise. Then Jochebed had a clever plan.

She put her baby in a waterproof basket and hid him in the reeds by the River Nile. She told his sister Miriam to watch and wait.

An Egyptian princess came to the river and saw the basket. When she found the baby boy inside, she knew she wanted to keep him.

'I will call him Moses,' she said.

Miriam was delighted! She told the princess she knew a woman who would look after the baby until he was big enough to live in the palace. And Miriam went to get her mother!

17

Flies, boils and locusts

When Moses grew up to be a man, God spoke to him from a bush burning in the desert.

'Go to the king of Egypt,' said God. 'Tell him to let my people go!'

Moses was afraid. He didn't want to go to the king! So God told him to take his brother Aaron with him to help.

Moses went with Aaron to give the king God's message. But the king was angry. He wouldn't let the people go. Instead he told the slave drivers to make them work even harder!

So God sent ten terrible plagues on the people of Egypt.

First the River Nile was turned as red as blood. Then there were frogs, everywhere there were frogs – in the houses, the food and the beds! Then the air was full of gnats, itching and biting; then buzzing flies.

All the horses, donkeys and camels, and cattle, sheep and goats became ill and died. Then the people were covered with nasty black boils so they couldn't stand up; and there was a terrible hailstorm that destroyed all the new crops and stripped the leaves from the trees. Locusts came later and ate anything and everything that was still left. Then the land was still and covered in complete darkness for three days.

God kept his people safe during this time. And when each plague happened, the king of Egypt agreed to let God's people go. But as soon as the plague was over, the king changed his mind.

Finally the tenth and most terrible of all the plagues came on the people of Egypt. God told Moses to get the people ready to leave. They put a special sign on their doors and ate a final meal of roast lamb with herbs, with their bags packed and their cloaks and shoes on.

That night every first-born male animal and every first-born son in Egypt died, including the king's son.

The king of Egypt sent for Moses.

'Take God's people, and go!' he shouted.

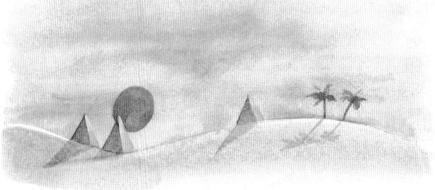

Ten rules for life

God looked after his people as they wandered in the desert. He also gave Moses rules so his people could live the way he wanted them to.

I am the Lord your God,
who rescued you when you were slaves in Egypt.
Don't talk to any other gods instead of me.
Don't pray to statues,
pictures of the earth, sky or sea, instead of me.

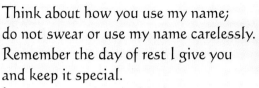

Think about how you use my name;
do not swear or use my name carelessly.
Remember the day of rest I give you
and keep it special.
Love your mother and father
and listen to what they say.
Do not plot to kill anyone.
Be faithful to your husband or wife.
Do not steal.
Do not tell lies about other people.
Don't look greedily
at things that belong to other people.

Published in the UK by Authentic Media Ltd
PO Box 6326, Bletchley, Milton Keynes MK1 9GG

ISBN 978-1-78893-052-9

First edition 2019

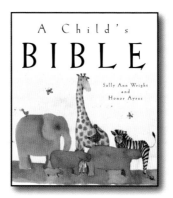

This is the first part of a selection of stories from
A Child's Bible, published in the UK by Authentic Media

ISBN 978-1-86024-855-9

www.authenticmedia.co.uk